He is the Rock, his works are perfect.
Deuteronomy 32:4

Up Sandy Hill, Down Rocky Canyon

The Great Pyramid of Giza

I am building my life on the Rock.

Worship the LORD with gladness.
Psalm 100:2

How do YOU see the world?

Great and marvelous are your deeds, Lord God Almighty. Just and true are your ways.
Revelation 15:3

Hiking up Bear Creek Trail

Did the brownies bake themselves?

How can we know what is true?

God speaks truth to me through His creation.

Jesus came to show us what God is like.

Obedience is doing what I am told with a willing and a loving heart.

"Wow, that's the coolest movie I've ever seen!"

In the Chronicles of Narnia, the lion Aslan represents Jesus Christ.
In the Bible, Jesus is called the Lion of Judah.

"Like a scarecrow in a melon patch, their idols cannot speak. . . .
Do not fear them; they can do no harm nor can they do any good."
Jeremiah 10:5

God spoke to Moses from a burning bush. Does that mean God looks like a bush? No!

God, your thoughts are precious to me. They are so many!
If I could count them, they would be more than all the grains of sand.
Psalm 139:17–18 (ICB)

"The LORD your God is with you, he is mighty to save. He will take great delight in you, he will quiet you with his love, he will rejoice over you with singing."
Zephaniah 3:17

"As for God, his way is perfect; the word of the LORD is flawless.
He is a shield for all who take refuge in him."
2 Samuel 22:31

God is eternal, meaning He has no beginning and no end.
How can a ring be a symbol of eternity?

People change, but God never changes.

The eyes of the LORD are everywhere, keeping watch on the wicked and the good.
Proverbs 15:3

Rembrandt's "Christ in the Storm on the Lake"

For God is greater than our hearts, and he knows everything.
1 John 3:20

How is your worldview like a cake?

Patrick, the patron saint of Ireland, is said to have used a three-leaf clover, or shamrock, to teach people about the Trinity.

Although each waterfall is unique, each is still part of the one river. God the Father, Son, and Holy Spirit are unique Persons, but they are still the one true God.

God the Father, as imagined by Michelangelo

Jesus is the "only begotten" Son of God the Father.

The Holy Spirit helps me to be more like Jesus.

The wolf will live with the lamb . . . the calf and the lion and the yearling together;
and a little child will lead them.
Isaiah 11:6

Hiking along Cougar River

Ben chooses to believe in God.

God created everything out of nothing by the mere power of His words.

Sadly, Adam and Eve chose not to believe God.

When we live in harmony with other Christians, the world
sees what life would be like if they, too, followed Jesus.

Father Damien shared God's love.

Teki hears a new song.

Parents have children because they want to give them love.

Everything was created for the enjoyment of God—including me!

Our Father, which art in heaven, Hallowed be Thy Name. Thy kingdom come, Thy will be done on earth, as it is in heaven.

I can glorify God by telling others about Him.

King David "danced before the Lord with all His might" (2 Samuel 6:14).

God wants me to be filled with joy every day.

Kalani and her parents pray for rain.

Island Gold

Every good and perfect gift comes from God.

God provides for all my physical needs.

God provides for all my non-physical needs.

I lift up my eyes to the hills—
where does my help come from?
My help comes from the LORD,
the Maker of heaven and earth.
Psalm 121:1–2

God sent ravens to bring food to the prophet Elijah.

Island Fire

Everything was perfect in the Garden of Eden.

Sin keeps us from God.

Joseph's brothers were jealous of him. Their jealousy grew into hatred.

As he approached Jerusalem and saw the city, he wept over it and said,
"If you . . . had only known on this day what would bring you peace . . ."
Luke 19:41–42

"The LORD has told you . . . what he wants from you: Do what is right to other people. Love being kind to others. And live humbly, trusting your God."
Micah 6:8 (ICB)

The mango is the world's most popular tropical fruit.

Island Praise

Fanny Crosby shares her poems of faith with the United States Congress.

Jesus' suffering was a terrible price to pay for our freedom—
more terrible than we can imagine.

"He is not here; he has risen, just as he said."
Matthew 28:6

Will you accept God's free gift of forgiveness and salvation?

What part will you play in God's great story?